The Feelings Book

TODD PARR

SCHOLASTIC INC.

ISBN 978-1-338-03395-3

12 11 10 9   17 18 19 20 21

Printed in the U.S.A.   40

First Scholastic printing, February 2016

This book is dedicated to
Dad, Tammy, Sandy, Sara, Dawn, Bryan, Bill,
Candy, Jerry, Liz and Gerry, John and Linda
Alioto, Maggie W., Jeff and Steve, Jim and
Jean, Bully, Mow, Isabel and Benny, Michael,
Artt, Megan, Cindy Sue, Kerri, Stacey, Linda,
and everyone at Little, Brown.

Love,
Todd

Sometimes I feel silly

Sometimes I feel cranky

Sometimes I feel scared

Sometimes I feel like standing on my head

Sometimes I feel like reading
a book under the covers

Sometimes I feel like celebrating my birthday

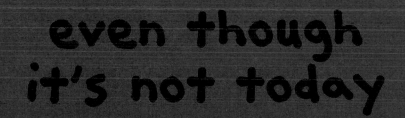

even though
it's not today

Sometimes I feel brave

Sometimes I feel like looking out the window all day

Sometimes I feel

like dancing

Sometimes I feel
like making mudpies

Sometimes I feel like I have a tummy ache

Sometimes I feel like holding hands with a friend

Sometimes I feel lonely

Sometimes I feel like yelling really loud

Sometimes I feel like staying in the bathtub all day

Sometimes I feel like trying something new

Sometimes I feel like dressing up

Sometimes I feel

like doing nothing

Sometimes I feel like camping with my dog

BULLY

Sometimes I feel like crying

Sometimes I feel like eating pizza for breakfast

Sometimes I feel like kissing a sea lion

Sometimes I feel
like a king

No matter how you feel, don't keep your feelings to yourself. Share them with someone you love.

Love,
Todd